BY WALT KELLY

SIMON AND SCHUSTER · NEW YORK

FABLE OF CONTENTS

*It should be borne in mind that at the time *we* were study-
ing *bats, bats* had an excellent opportunity to study *us*.

DISCLAIMER

MOST BOOKS are dedicated to some person—a friend, relative, customer, sweetheart, animal, vegetable, or mineral. It would, however, be unjust to fix the responsibility for the material herein contained on anyone in particular.

Practically everybody that Kelly knows or has ever met is equally guilty. His own mother is not entirely blameless. She early aided and abetted him, never broke him to the muzzle or the leash. His father, an otherwise virtuous man, taught him how to draw. His sister sharpened his pencils and corrected his spelling. These misdemeanors were compounded by later associates, many of whom, masquerading as school teachers, encouraged him in a shameless manner. Newspapermen, artists, writers, and Hollywood animators taught him the rudiments of anti-social behavior until he became fit for nothing but comic strip work.

As a result, it should be stressed that the fault here lies not so much with Kelly, who is merely an easily influenced youth on the sunny side of thirty-nine, but with his associates, early and late. It should be further stressed that Kelly's companions being what they are, most of them have been late most of the time.

Speaking for himself (a steady habit of his), Kelly declines to be responsible (another steady habit) for this exhibition.

A WOMAN HAS ONLY ACUMEN

BUT A GOOD CIGAR IS A SMOKE

2

OH ME! I'D DO *ANYTHING* TO SQUARE THE INSULT TO YOU TURTLES.

WHY, *NATURAL!* US TURTLES FORGIVES YOU IF YOU *SWEARS* TO DO *ANYTHING!*

HA! WE GOT HIM!

OWL, YOU ISN'T A *TURTLE!* YOU IS A FEATHERED CRITTUR --- --- TURTLES IS WET AN' SLIPPERY.

OL' OWL BE SLIPPERY AS THEY COME --- GO AHEAD AN' SWEAR, POGO.

POGO POSSUM, YOU IS INSULTED THE TURTLE RACE --- SO YOU OUGHT TO *SWEAR TO DO ANYTHING WE SAY!*

NOSSIR! YOU LI'L SCAPERS IS UP TO SOME DEVILMINTS.

THE CITY OF NASHVILLE

OOOOH! YOU SAY YOU GONE *EAT MUD TURTLES!* I NEVER SO *IN*SULTED IN MY NATURAL BORN LIFE.

ME, TOO.

I WOULDN'T EAT A TURTLE IF YOU WAS THE LAST PERSON ON EARTH.

WHAT?! ANOTHER INSULT!

YOOHF! WATER! WATER! *NOW* US TURTLES IS INSULTED FORE AND AFT! US CAN'T BEAR SUCH IGNOMINNIES.

OH GALL! BITTER, BITTER WORMWOODS.

THE CITY OF NASH

4

AHEM!

OL' OWL WILL NOW GIVE US A FEW *CHOICE* WORDS.

WHAT WAS WRONG WITH *MY* CHOICE?

THE CITY OF NASHVILLE

LADIES, GENTLEMEN, AND FRIENDS OF THE TURTLES, I RISE TO GIVE Y'ALL WELCOME.

HEAR! HEAR! HEAR! GREAT! GREAT!

THE CITY OF NASHVILLE

IF THE GENTLEMAN FROM OKEFENOKEE WILL PLEASE REE-STRAIN HIS ENTHUSIASM---?

I WILL APPLAUD BY WINGLIN' MY FINGERBONES.

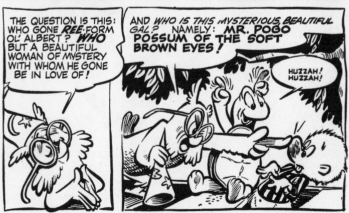

THE QUESTION IS THIS: WHO GONE *REE*-FORM OL' ALBERT? *WHO* BUT A BEAUTIFUL WOMAN OF MYSTERY WITH WHOM HE GONE BE IN LOVE OF!

AND *WHO IS THIS MYSTERIOUS, BEAUTIFUL GAL?* NAMELY: MR. POGO POSSUM OF THE SOFT BROWN EYES!

HUZZAH! HUZZAH!

YOU WANTS ME TO DRESS UP LIKE A MYSTERIOUS AN' BEAUTIFUL GAL TO CONVINCE ALBERT HE OUGHT TO GIVE UP SEEGARS---SO'S *YOU TWO* SCAMPS CAN SMOKE 'EM--- I CAN'T DO IT.

TUSH! WE GOT YOUR PROMISE.

I GOT THE DISGUISE! A MOP, A COAT AN' A BASKET.

POGO

BEAUTIFUL I MAY BE-- EVEN MYSTERIOUS-- BUT I ISN'T NO GAL.

DAZZLIN'*! BLINDIN' BEAUTY!* WE COVERS OUR PEEPERS 'FORE WE FALLS IN LOVE WITH YOU OUR OWN SELFS!

IS YOU COVERIN' YO' EYEBALLS OR HOLDIN' YO' NOSES?

GO AHEAD, WALK 'ROUND TO ALBERT'S HOUSE---US WILL SCURRY 'ROUND THE SHORT WAY TO PREPARE HIM FO' YO' VISIT.

A Mere Meanwhile away.

WELL! IF IT ISN'T THE REAL McGEE, THE SUBSTITUTE MAIL MAN.

UNCLE REGULAR CURTIS IS SICK --- GOT A LETTER FO' YOU, ALBERT.

READ IT SOME.

LET'S SEE · FIRST WE GOT A "X" OR POSSIBLE A "B". THEM "B" BOYS CREEPS IN EV'Y WHERE. GOTTA WATCH 'EM --- THEN A COUPLE "R'S" AN' A PASSEL OF LI'L BITTY THINGS LIKE ANTS.

PHOO! THAT ALL THE READIN' YOU GONE DO?

WHAT YOU WANTS FROM THE CIVIL SERVICE? SINGIN' AN' DANCIN'?

ALBERT! ALBERT! WONDERFUL NEWS!

I GOT ALL THE NEWS I CAN STAND BUT I CAN'T READ IT.

I BET I IS *RAVISHIN'* FIT TO KILL!

WARN THE GENTRY! THE *PEST HOUSE* MUST OF IS DONE *BUST LOOSE!*

A HIGH CLASS GAL LIKE STRAWBERRY SHORTCUT WILL WANT YOU TO GIVE UP SEEGARS SO I WILL JUS' HOLD THE BOX.

HERE SHE COME!

EL FALFA 20 for 5¢

HOT DOG! THEY IS *BOTH* SPEECHLESS!

H'LO THERE, BIG BOY. I IS STRAWBERRY SHORTCUT, THE BATON ROUGE BOMB SHELL-- WHY DON'T YOU GIVE UP SEEGARS?

GOOD WORK, POGO.

JUS' A MINUTE, BROWN EYES - I GONE SIGN THE PLEDGE 'GAINST SMOKIN'.

MAN! I IS A *NATURAL BORN SYREEN.*

10

11

12

SHO', I'LL GIVE YO' A RIDE, SEMINOLE SAM, BUT DON'T TRY TO SELL ME NONE OF THAT EE-LIXIR; IT'S PLAIN WATER.

NOSSIR -- HOWEVER, HOW'D YOU LIKE TO BUY A SLICE OF TORONTO?

TORONTO BELONGS TO CANADA, ALBERT

INCREDIBLE! AND I BOUGHT IT FROM SUCH A NICE OLD COUPLE IN FORT WORTH -- SAID IT WAS IN THE STATE!

WELL, UNTIL I CAN CLEAR MY DEED, HOW ABOUT A SMALL FLASK OF DRY WATER? SEE, I POUR IT OUT AND MY HAND REMAINS DRY.

NO WONDER! THERE'S NOTHIN' IN THE BOTTLE!

NATURALLY -- I JUST EMPTIED IT IN THE DEMONSTRATION --- HOW'D YOU LIKE TO HAVE THE DRY WATER CONCESSION FOR THE ATLANTIC OCEAN? YOU COULD RUN OFF THE WET WATER, POUR IN THE DRY AND RENT THE BOTTOM OUT FOR A PARKIN' LOT.

OH, GOODY.

COME ON AN' HELP ME POLE THROUGH THIS OL' SWAMP GRASS, SAM.

OOP! WE IS PUSHIN' THE OL' SCOW OUT FROM UNDERNEATH OF US! THE OL' POLE IS STUCK IN THE MUD.

15

WE'RE DOOMED! **DOOMED!** DOOMED TO SPEND THE REST OF OUR LIVES ON THIS POLE---- WE'LL SHRIVEL AND GENTLY FALL LIKE LOVELY AUTUMN LEAVES.

YOU IS MORE THE LOVELY HICK'RY NUT TYPE, DOCTOR.... SO STAY THERE 'TIL YOU RIPE. I GONE STROLL OVER TO THIS SWAMP ISLAND AND SET MY LOVELY SELF DOWN.

'LONG AS YOU IS CATCHIN' A **FISH** AN' BUILDIN' A **FIRE**, I'LL COME ALONG AN' GIVE YOU **AD**VICE.

WELL, HERE WE ARE! **MAROONED** ON A DESERT ISLAND, WE'LL **STARVE!**

I WON'T STARVE.

MY FRIEND, I ADMIRE YOUR DEXTERITY CATCHING THAT FISH---- HOWEVER, IF I MAY MAKE A SUGGESTION, YOU USE MUCH TOO LONG A STICK TO BROIL IT.

MUCH TOO?

22

SCIENCE ALWAYS FINDS A WAY! PSYCHOLOWOGGY WILL ROUSE THEM LI'L OL' MICE OUTEN YO' INNARDS, ALBERT.

GOT AS MUCH RIGHT HERE AS ANY-BODY.

ROGER! THAT'S ME.

I'VE TRAINED ROGER TO DEECOY THEM OUT. HE'LL TALK 'EM INTO LEAVIN' ----- GO IT, ROGER!

HEY! IT'S ROGER! GREAT! NOW WE'VE GOT A FOURTH. CUT THE CARDS, CHARLES.

WHOSE DEAL?

DON'T FEEL BAD, OWL. IT'S BETTER'N THEM PLAYIN' HIDE AND SEEK. MAN! ALL THAT OL' RUNNIN' AROUND! THEY GOT THE COLDEST LITTLE FEET THIS SIDE OF LAPLAND!

STILL, ROGER DISAPPOINTS ME.

SCIENCE WILL FIND A WAY! JUSTICE WILL TRIUMPH! I WILL GET 'EM OUT.

HERE Y'ARE, ALBERT! OPEN WIDE. MAN! THIS GONE BE LIKE SHOOTIN' FISH IN A BARREL.

SPLASH!

ALBERT *REALLY* 'PRECIATES WHAT YOU DOIN', OWL -- HE JUST TOUCHY RIGHT NOW.

BUT *WHY* DO HE FLING MY BLUNDY-BUSTER OVERBOARD?

MEBBE I CAN COAX YOUR MICE OUT WITH SOME GOODIES.

LET'S PLAY HIDE AND SEEK AGAIN

YOU'RE IT

HMM -- NEVER THOUGHT OF FISHIN' IN *THERE* --- WHAT YOU AFTER, POGO?

MICE, PORKYPINE.

MICE?

MICE.

OKAY - SO IT'S MICE --- I GUESS THAT'S A PRETTY FUNNY ANSWER. *SOMEHOW, THE HUMOR IN THIS STRIP ELUDES ME.*

IF THEM MICE WON'T COME OUT ANY OTHER WAY, ALBERT, WE'LL *TRAP* 'EM!

GOOD! I HEARD IT CLICK ON *SOMETHIN'*!

ONLY THING YOU GOT WAS MY SEEGAR.

PHOO! JUST IN TIME! WE QUIT! YOU SMOKED US OUT! WE CAN'T STAND NO MORE OF YO' SEEGARS.

LET'S GO BACK TO THAT JOB WE HAD IN THE NURSERY RHYME ~~~

HICKORY DICKORY, *PARLEZ-VOUS?*

FOUR-FLUSHING
The
GROUND HOG
FROM COVER TO COVER

28

WOOP! YOU'RE NOT SO LI'L AND CUTE, NOR SO CUDDABLE AN' LOVABOBBLE ARE YOU?

HMMPH! JUST LEMME EXAMINE **YOU** IN THE LIGHT, SON!

PHOOF! YOU ISN'T NO SIGHT FOR SORE EYES EITHER, YOU HOUND ANIMAL, YOU!

MAN! NOW I *KNOW* WHY THEY *CALLS* EM GROUN' HOGS -- HE SHO' HOGS A MESS OF GROUN'.

NO, THAT ISN'T MY SPECIALTY.

BLESS MY SOFT BROWN EYES! IF YOU WAS LOOKIN' FO' A *GROUN'* HOG, YOU HAD ONE WITH YOU -- OL' *GEORGE WOODCHUNK*

A *SNEAKY* TRICK! GOIN' AROUN' CALLIN' YOURSELF A **WOODCHUNK**. HOW 'BOUT WINTER? GONE BE MUCH MORE OF IT ?

WELL, UH-- IT'S THIS WAY... UH OOOP!

THERE HE GO! HE'S SEED HIS SHADOW ... HOWDY, MIS' WOOD' CHUNK!

'TWEEN YOU AND ME, ALBERT, OL' GEORGE EE-LUDES TH' PORE WOMAN ALL WINTER BY *HIGH-BERNATIN'* --HAW! ACTUAL HE PLAYIN' PEA-KNUCKLE AT THE FIREHOUSE.

MADAM, DO THIS MEAN SIX MORE WEEKS OF WINTER?

NOT IF I KETCH HIM! SPRING CLEANIN' GONE START RIGHT OFF WITH *HIM!*

SOME
OLD EGGS
IN A NEW
BASKET

WE IS GONNA MARCH ON *WASHINGTON* AND DEMAND TO SEE THE *EASTER BUNNY.*

WHY? *EASTER* ISN'T HERE.

BUT WE IS! AN' WE WANTS TO MAKE SURE OUR PUBLIC SERVANTS IS—

"AS *READY* AS *US!*"

THAT'S SURE EXORCISIN' YOUR CIVIL RIGHTS.

IT'S A CRY AN' SHAME— OL' *EASTER BUNNY* IS *NOWHERE* ROUND— I WILL PERSONAL *DRESS* UP LIKE THE RABBIT IN A OL' *BUNNY* SUIT I WEARS ON COLD NIGHTS.

CAN'T JES' LEAVE THE CHILLUN GO WITHOUT *EASTER EGGS*— *SAY,* WHERE DO THE OL' *BUNNY* *GIT* THEM EGGS?

STRONG OL' LEGEND SAY HE PLAIN *LAYS 'EM* PERSONAL.

33

HERE'S THE BOTTLES, ALBERT, ALL'S I COULD GIT IS TWO.

TWO'S BE PLENTY.

YOU MIND IF I GOES **HOME** TO SUPPER, ALBERT?

GLOMPF!

WELL, *POP* MY CORN! LI'L BABY 'GATORS... MY! THEY SURE LOOKS LIKE THEIR UNCLE ALBERT.

NEVER MIND THE FOOLISHMINTS -- THESE IS BIRDS.

BIRDS! WHY PAMPER THEM, MAN!? GIT 'EM OUT OF THE NEST-- **TEACH 'EM** TO FLY!?

YOU TEACH 'EM. YOU IS MORE THE SHOO-FLY TYPE--

NOW, BIRD BABIES, WATCH ME SHOW YOU HOW TO FLY --- OL' OWL ISN'T VERY GOOD AT IT ---HE'S TOO RUSTY---

ONE-TWO FLAP--- ONE-TWO FLAP--

39

HOW TO THANK ALBERT? *I KNOW*, WE'LL BE LIKE **CROCODILE** BIRDS WHAT KEEP THE CROCODILE'S TEETH CLEAN BY PLUCKIN' TIDBITS OUTEN THEM.

CAREFUL, MIZ GRACKLE, *THAT* IS ALBERT'S **TONGUE**.

WHAT A PITY--- IT'S SUCH A *BIG* PIECE.

PLUCK EASY YOU LI'L' DENTAL HYENAS.

IS YOU THRU PICKIN' ALBERT'S TEETH LIKE A CROCODILE BIRD, MIZ GRACKLE?

YEP AN' LONG AS 'T RAININ', I'LL LEAVE TH' CHILLUN INDOORS AN' I VISITS AUNT PANSY.

GONE SNEEZE! UGH--OOP HUB--- *HUGGEE AH~ AH~*

NOT NOW! NOT NOW!

CHOO!

LOOKY THERE, PANSY! MY LI'L' SHIRT TAIL TADS FLEW OVER BY THEMSELVES *NO HANDS!* AN' WITH LESS FEATHERS 'TWEEN 'EM THAN YOU FIND IN A NEST OF MUD TURKLES

TALENT RUN IN THE FAMBLY.

40

SOME GENTLEMEN
of the
FOURTH
ESCAPE

THING I LIKE 'BOUT CHURCHY'S BARBER SHOP IS READIN 'BOUT THESE MURDERS AN' FIGHTS IN THE COMICAL BOOKS.

MAN, HERE'S A NEWSPAPER WHAT SAY: "WET SPELL COMIN'---THE ALAPAHA IS OVERFLOWIN'---THE SUWANEE IS RAGIN'"---

---THE SATILLA IS A TORRENT---THE ALTAMAHA IS A-BOIL---THE OGEECHEE IS---*HEY, WHAT*---?

FLOOD! FLOOD! *FLOOD!* FLOOD! FLOOD!

AS I WAS ABOUT TO SAY, "THE OL' OGEECHEE'S A MERE *TRINKLE*, AND THINGS ISN'T TOO DANGEROUS." BESIDES THIS PAPER IS FOR MARCH 3, NINETEEN FOURTEEN.

THAT SCARE WE HAD 'BOUT THE FLOOD SHOWS HOW US NEEDS A *REAL* NEWS-*PAPER* -- SHOO, BIRD, **SHOO** -- NO NEED TO HIDE IN THE MANDOLIN, NOW.

CRITTURS WHAT RUNS NEWSPAPERS MAKES *MILLIONS.*

OUT OUT OUT OUT!

MILLIONS?

ZZZZ UM-BPSZ CUMQUOT ZZZZ

SURE, MILLIONS ---- MAYBE EVEN *THOUSANDS* WHO *KNOWS? HUNDREDS* MAY WELL BE INVOLVED.

WELL! NOTICE ANYTHING DIFFERENT ABOUT ME? I IS *JUST* GONE INTO THE NEWSPAPER BUSINESS.... ---- YOU GOT A SPARE PENCIL AND A WRITIN' PAD TO HOME?

WHY THE VISOR, MR EDITOR?

NATURAL, IT'S TO KEEP THE WAX OUTEN MY EYES.

NEWSPAPER OFS

NEWSPAPERS GOTTA HAVE *LEGMEN* TO REPORT THE NEWS WE GOT THE *LEGGIEST* VARMINTS I *EVER* SEE. GIT ON OUT AND GRAB SOME SCANDAL, BOYS.

COMIC STRIP!?

THIS IS NO COMIC STRIP!

NEWSPAPER OFIS

THIS IS THE STORY OF MY *LIFE* --- IN PICTURES! FRAUGHT WITH FARCE --- --TRAPPED IN TRAGEDY-- DECKED WITH DESPAIR-- REPLETE WITH RUE! WELL, I'LL SEE THE BOYS AT THE SMITHSONIAN. GOOD DAY!

REPLETE WITH *RUE?*

I REPEAT: REE-PLETE!

D'YOU THINK I WOULD MAKE A GOOD COPY-READER?

USE TO BE A NEWSPAPER MAN MYSELF -- WHAT YOU GOT TO DO IS ATTACH YOURSELF TO THE STAFF.

MAN SAY A-TTACH -- SO A-TTACH IT IS

WHAT'LL I DO NOW? WOTTLE I DO NOW --- WOTTLY DOONOW WOLLYDOONA WOLLYDO WOLL DO WOL DO WOOO WO W

AS A OL' NEWSPAPER MAN I SAY: DON'T TALK WITH YOUR MOUTH FULL.

THIS BUG ATTACHED HISSELF TO THE STAFF BY CLAMPIN' HIS JAWBONES ONTO MY PERSONAL TAIL! HOW I GITS HIM OFF?

HAND YOUR TAIL HERE

NIX NIX NIX! I WANTS TO *KEEP* THAT PART.

I MEANS TO CUT LOOSE THE BUG LESSEN HE LET GO---AH--- HERE HE COME!

PHOO! WELL, NOW WHAT YOU GOT TO SUGGEST, YOU OLD NEWS-PAPER MAN?

GO BACK IN THERE AND GET SEVERANCE PAY!

I HAVE RETURNED! LAST WEEK YOU REFUSED THE SAD STORY OF MY LIFE AN' CALLED IT A COMIC STRIP! I HAVE COME BACK! REVENGE SHALL BE MINE.

DON'T BE HASTY NOW, OL' PORKYPINE

JUST WAIT.

NO UNSOLICITED CONTRIBUTIONS LIKE FIREARMS OR BOMBS---LOUD NOISES SCARE US.

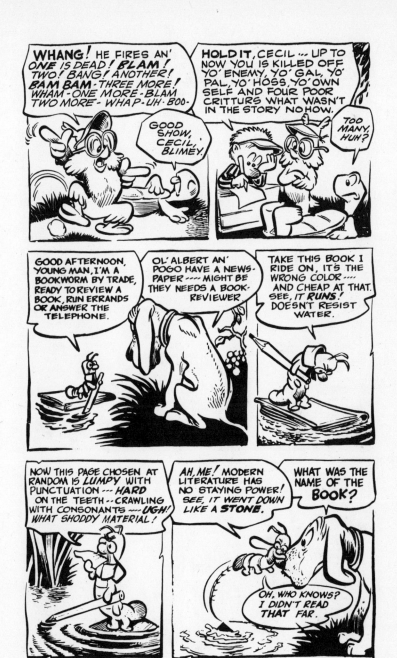

49

POGO, I GITTIN' TIRED OF THE NEWSPAPER BUSINESS --- SAY! LET ME TRY THAT!

NO WONDER YOU IS A GOOD SPELLER! YOU GOT A LI'L SPELLIN' MACHINE!

AAH! THIS BLACK-STAGGERED LI'L BLAGGARD IS SNAGGED MY FINGERBONE!

ARRGHFF! YOU BOG STOMPIN' TREECHEROUS LI'L SNEAK! YOU AMBUSHED ME! LEGGO! LEGGO!

WELL, ALBERT, THAT PUTS US OUT OF BUSINESS ALL RIGHT-- YOU IS SMASHED OUR ONLY PRESS TO BITS.

AN' NOT ANY TOO SOON! THE FREEDOM OF THAT PRESS GOT SO FAR OUT OF HAND WE MIGHT ALL OF BEEN CON-SOOMED!

HEY, POGO, COME AN' WATCH MY FRIEND, THE BOOK WORM, HE'S REVIEWIN' A BOOK FOR YOUR NEWSPAPER.

BUT, WE IS OUT OF BUSINESS.

IT'S JUST AS WELL ---THIS BOOK WILL NEVER GET BY-- ITS PACE IS ALL WRONG-- --THE PLOT IS DISJOINTED-- --THE CHARACTERS ARE WEAK ITS SPELLING IS BAD!

UPON ATOM

THAT'S THE ADVANTAGE OF THIS TYPE BOMB-- A ATOM BOMB CAN PUT EVERYTHING ALL OVER NOWHERE! --NOTHIN' TO SWEEP UP...

NO MUSS, EH?

ABSOLOOSELY NO MUSS--- SOLVES YOUR PROBLEM.

GLAD OF THAT, THO' IT'S NOT EGGS-ZACKLY THE PROBLEM I HAD IN MIND.

PSSST-- BUGS, YOU OKAY?

WELL, I GLAD YOU IS FINALLY PUNCHIN' HOLES IN THAT BOX TO GIVE THEM ADAM BUGS SOME AIR.

FOOSH --- THIS HOLE IS FOR THE BOMB'S FUSE.

BOOK SAY: WHEN YOU SPLITS AN ATOM, IT--

SPLITS A ADAM!? OWL, YOU ISN'T GONE USE THEM FRIENDLY BUGS FOR BAIT?

WHAT A IGNORAM-BUMPTIOUS YOUTH! BAIT IN-DEED! POGO, YOU JUS' DON'T UNDERSTAND 'BOUT FISSION A —TALL---

SO!

I KNOWS THIS MUCH 'BOUT FISHIN' OWL --- WHEN YOU USES A CRITTUR FOR BAIT, IT SORT OF SPOILS HIM FOR ANYTHING ELSE -- AN' I ISN'T GONE LET YOU DO IT TO THE OL' ADAM FAMILY.

WHY, POGO!

54

55

OL' OWL CLAIM HE MAKIN' A **ADAM BOMB** --- **HAW HAW** --- HE CAN'T PULL MY WOOL OVER THE ICE --- HE UP TO **SOMETHIN'.**

I BLEEVE HE'S **PREE** PARIN' A BIG OL' **LUNCH** -- **HAW!** I WILL SPY OUT HIS SECRET -- HE'LL NEVER KNOW ME AS A OL' **SIZZLE GRINDER.**

DOG MY CATS! A HANDSOME MAN LOOKS GOOD IN ANYTHING --- I SHOULD OF BEEN A ACTOR -- **MIGHT** OF **BEEN ANOTHER RING-TING-TING** -- MY **DISGUISE** IS IMPENATRABOBBLE!

H'LO, LI'L FROG TADS.

H'LO, ALBERT --- YOU COTCH YO' HEAD IN A **GRACKLE** NEST?

THERE GO TURTLE, UP TO OWL'S HOUSE. NOW I'LL SEE IF THEY IS TRYIN' TO HIDE SOME GOODIES.

CHURCHY, WE IS GONE MAKE A **ADAM BOMB** --- IT'S ALL THE RAGE --- YOU ALL SET TO FIGGER, FELLOW-SINUS?

YEP, I BRINGS MY **EE-RASER**

NOW IF YOU SPLITS A ADAM BY DIVIDIN' HALF THE PARALLELO-GRAM CRACKIES WITH THE HIPPO**POTE**NUSE, YOU TURNS OFF THE **RADIO** ONTO THE **ANGLE**WORM OF THE ···

HOLD IT··· FELLOW-SINUS! *HOLD IT, BOY!*

MEBBE HIPPOPOTENEESE DON'T LIKE *GRAM CRACKIES*.-*BESIDES* THEY IS *FAT* AN' *SCAREY* AN' MIGHTY NIGH AS *FIERCER* NOR A *RHINOCER*-WURST.

RIGHT! I WILL *REE*-MOVE THE CENTER-FRUGALS

MAN SAY ONE TIME THAT ADAMS IS INDIVISIBLE ··· *HAW* -SCIENCE IS PROVED *OTHER*WISE·· TAKE A NOTE, CHURCHY.

FIRST: **ADAMS** IS *NOT IN-DIVISIBLE* ···MAINLY NAMELY 'CAUSE *I* IS SEED THE LI'L ADAM BUGS WITH MY OWN *EAGLE-TYPE EYE BALLS, HARRUMPH!*

HOW YOU SPELLS THAT "HARRUMPH"?

NOW, TO SEE IF THEY IS PACKIN' SANWICHES. THEY'LL NEVER KNOW ME DISGUISED AS A SIZZLE GRINDER.

HEY! SHARPEN 'EM UP TODAY?

YOWP.! A FOREIGN POWER! EAT THE NOTES EAT THE NOTES.

57

58

Panel 1: I KNOWS! I KNOWS! YOU CROSSES 'EM AN' YOU GITS TO THE OTHER SIDE.

Panel 2: HOW *REE-DICULOST!* IF YOU CROSS THESE, *YOU GITS A YEW-RANIUM* BUSH!

Panel 3: HMMPH

WELL, DR. LYSENKO, *WE BEEN WAITIN'* HALF A HOUR--- MEBBE IF WE CROSSES OUR FINGERS, TOO?

Panel 4: THE NATURAL BORN REASON WE DIDN'T GIT NO YEW-RANIUM WHEN WE CROSSES THE LI'L *YEW* TREE AND THE GEE-RANIUM IS *ON* ACCOUNT OF CAUSE WE DIDN'T HAVE NO *GEIGER* COUNTER

WHAT FO' WE *NEEDS* ONE?

Panel 5: TO COUNT THE LI'L GEIGERS, *NATURAL*. TAKE THE COUNTER NOW-- WE TRIES IT AGAIN ----

Panel 6: I READY TO COUNT--- CHASE THEM GEIGERS PAST - *OH GEIGER GOOGER ROOTER BAGGER OLE!*

WAIT--- *WHO YOU?*

A LI'L PLANT LICE---

Panel 7: NAME OF GEIGER?

IS YOU *RADIO-ACTIVE?*

NOT SO ACTIVE. NAME IS FRED AN' IT'S ON TH' WAITIN' LIST AT *NBC* AND *CBS* --- BUT NOBODY IS USIN' CRICKET IMITATIONS THESE DAYS.

59

I GONE UP AGAIN AN' SEE WHAT KIND OF GOODIES THEY IS **EATIN'** TO THEMSELVES.

NOW GIT A LOAD OF THE **CHAIN** REACTION WHEN I SOCKS IT WITH THE **ADAM** SMASHER.

WOCK!

MAN! WHAT A REACTION!

YARGH!

THE SIZZLE-GRIND MAN AGAIN--- AND DO **YOU** SEE WHAT **I** SEE?

YESSIR, FRIEND, I IS CONVINCED THAT OWL AN' TURTLE IS **HOARDIN'** A **TREE**-MOUNDOUS LUNCH AN' WON'T GIVE **US** ANY A-TALL!

ALL THEM NOTES I MADE IS SORTA HOM**OGEN**ATED-- MOSTLY I GOT A MESS OF "B's"-- A FEW GRAVY SPECKLES AN' A COUPLE SAMMY COLONS.

"B's" HMM

"B's GIVE ME A IDEA --- C'MERE CAP'N LA FEMME.

HOLE OPEN THE BOX, SON --- *BEES* IS MIGHTY NIGH AS SMALL AS THE *ADAMS BUGS* AND THEY IS A PECK MORE *EXPLOSIVE* --- *WE GONE CONSTRUCT A "B" BOMB 'STEAD OF A "A" BOMB.*

NOW WE IS *REALLY* GOT A BOMB ---- A *BEE* BOMB WITH A WHOLE *BEE-HIVE* IN IT.

WE IS *LEADIN'* THE LEAGUE. I WILL HELP YOU DOWN THE LADDER, DOC.

YOWP!

AT LAST! WE CAPTURED THE LUNCH.

AND NOW, MR. SMART CATS, I IS GOT THE BIG OL' LUNCH AN' YOU CAN WATCH *ME DEE-VOUR* THE ----

NO --- WAIT!

LIKE THE MAN SAY, SON, *WAIT.*

I FIGGER IT BETTER TO *DEE-VIDE BEFORE* YO' *DEE-VOUR* --- RATHER 'N GO TO ALL THAT FUSS *AFTER* YOU EATS IT, BROWN EYES.

WALT KELLY

62

MY LOVE IS A ROSE OUR VIOLENCE BLUE; A YOUNG MAN'S FANCY AND SO, DEAR, ARE YOU

OLD CORNISH AIR

THIS LADY WHOM YOU WOO, PORKY, IS IT THE SAME WHO USED TO PLAY AT *SEE-SAW* WITH YOU?

NO! EVERY TIME I WAS LOW MAN ON THAT *TEETER BOARD*, SHE WOULD SLIDE DOWN TO *MY* END OF THE SEE-SAW.

WHOOSH! DOWN SHE *SWEPT!* HIT ME IN THE MIDDLE OF A FOUR BAR *DRONE* SOLO (WHICH I RATHER FANCIED)---WELL, FRIENDS, *THAT* TOOK THE WIND OUT OF *MY* BAGPIPES, I *MUST SAY!*

NOT ONLY *THAT*---BUT IN HER RECKLESS HASTE, SHE *PUNCHED* TWO TICKETS TO THE *1938 WARE COUNTY FAIR* THAT *I'D* BEEN SAVING IN MY HAT FOR A *RAINY DAY.*

WHAT A SORRY WASTE

THIS *NEW* LADY ACQUAINTANCE IS A DELIGHT TO THE EYE, POGO--- A VERY *QUEEN* OF LOVELINESS!

GEE GOSH

MMP!

HER *VOICE* IS THAT OF AN *ANGEL*-- HER *EYES* ARE LIKE *DEEP FOREST POOLS...*

HOT DOG!

BOY!

65

HOLD IT! *INTERLUDE OF SMALL ACTIVITY BACKSTAGE.*

WINNIPEG WAS OPEN, THE BURST AGAIN TO *SING*, OH, WORSE THAN THAT A *DANISH DITCH* WAS TWO-BY-FOUR THE *KING.*

YOU'RE *HIRED.*

YOU WANT US TO *START?*

WHAT'LL WE *PLAY?*

START FOR *AUSTRALIA* AND *PLAY* DOMINOES!

PORKYPINE DIN'T LIKE THE SONG US *SERENADERS* WROTE IN ORDER TO HELP HIM *COURT* HIS *LADY FRIEND*---LET'S PRACTICE A NEW ONE.

RIGHT

OH, THE PARSNIPS WERE *SNIPPING* THEIR SNAPPERS--- WHILE THE *PARSLEY* WAS *PARCELING* THE *PEAS*--- AND *PARSING* A *SENTENCE* FROM *HANDLE* TO *HAND* WAS A *HORNET* WHO HUMMED WITH THE *BEES.*

OH---

WAIT! WAIT! SOMETHIN' IS PLUGGED UP MY *SOUSAPHONE.*

AW, YOU'RE *FLAT* ANYHOWS.

NOT *HALF* AS *FLAT* AS *YOU* GONE BE IF YOU *DOESN'T* STOP SNEAKIN' INTO *REHEARSALS!*

MI MI MI

67

68

KINDA HARD TO FIT THAT INTO A SONG CALLED "*PING THE PONG BALL OF MY HEART, DEAR.*"

US COULD WORK IT OUT BETTER IF YOU KNEW'D A LADY NAME OF **LOU**---OR MEBBE **SUE**--- HOW ABOUT IT, POGO, **YOU** KNOW ANY **GALS** NAMED LIKE THAT?

COULD EVEN BE **SAM.**

GOSH, PORKYPINE IS GOIN' COURTIN' AT LAST.

AN' SHE IS BEAUTIFUL.

YEP, HE SAY SHE GOT **EYES** LIKE **POOLS.**

SAY SHE GOT A **VOICE** LIKE A **ANGEL.**

YEP. I SAID ALL THAT!

MAN, YOU MUST BE REAL **GENUINE IN LOVE!**

I IS NOT NEITHER!

THE LADY I VISIT JUST HAPPENS TO MAKE THE **BEST POPOVERS** THIS SIDE OF THE *CHATTAHOOCHIE* RIVER.

SO! PORKYPINE IS GONE OFF TO COURT A LADY NAME OF **HEPZIBAH**, WHAT IS A *GRADE A* COOK AN' BAKER!

TWO KIN PLAY AT *THAT* GAME, BY JING! OH SWEEP MISERY OF LIFE'S, LAST NIGHT I FINDS YO'!

ALBRT

PORKY DON'T KNOW IT, BUT HE GONE GIT A LI'L **NATURAL BORN COMPETITION!** WHERE'S THAT *CANDY* I WINNED AT THE **CHICAGO WORLD'S FAIR?**

Albert

COME ON! GIT OUTTA THERE, BOYS! I GOTTA TAKE THESE GOODIES TO THE **OBJECK** OF MY **AFFECTATIONS.**

WE'RE AT THE HOUSE WHERE DWELLS THE *LADY OF MY HEART*, POGO.

WHAT SHE LOOK LIKE, PORKY?

SHE'S THE CUTEST LI'L OL' **BLACK, FUR COLORED PORKYPINE** YOU EVER SEED.

A **ALL** BLACK PORKYPINE?

NOT *EN*TIRE ALL.

AH! JE SUIS ENCHANTE! THEES TIME, HERE EES *TWO* OF YOU PORKYPINIES, *NO?*

('SCUSE MY FRENCH, POGO--- WEE, MADAM-AN'-ZELLE, I EES BRANG TODAY ZE FRAN'!

PLAY ZEE "FLY-TOUGH-ZEE BUMBLEE BEANS," PORCHY!

KEEP CLEAR, POGO---I REALLY **RIPS** THRU **THIS** ONE!

YOO HOOS!

BEWARES! A *RHINOSSER-WOSSER!*

('SCUSE MY *FRENCH*, ALBERT---) MAM'SELLE HEPZIBAH, *THEES EES MY FRAN' WHAT GO BY ZEE NAME ALBAIRT!*

ALORS!

AH, MADAM-MY-ZELLE! OO ES LA CHATT DOO MAW GRAN' MEER?

QUELLE HORREURS! HERE EES AN *ESQUIMAUX,* NO?

ALBERT GOT A FRENCH A-B-C BOOK.

Candy

WHY, 'ALLO TODAY! HOW EES ZEE *POGO* TODAY AN' ZEE HOUND DOG *TODAY?*

HA!

'LO

I DON'T RIGHTLY SEE *WHAT* PORKY AN' ALBERT SEE IN---HUH---HMMM

PHOO--- NEITHER DO I--- ---UM---

♪ OH, MISS *HEPZIBAH!* ☼ UGH!

OH MISS *HEPZIBAH!* ☼ OWP!

OH, *GOODEE!* YOU EES SO SWEET, GARÇONS, TO FIND ZEE HONKYCHEEF OF MY FRAN', *MADAM BEAVAIR* WHO I HAVE LOST EET FOR HER!

AS I WAS SAYIN', I DON'T SEE SO MUCH IN MISS MAM'SELLE HEPZIBAH, *NOTHIN'* TO RAVE ABOUT."

COURSE NOT COURSE NOT COURSE NOT COURSE NOT

SORT OF DAMP OUT TODAY, POGO. GUESS WE'RE IN FOR A SPELL OF RAIN.

THAT SO? I ISN'T REALLY NOTICED.

AH! *POGOS!* EES EET THAT POGOS EES WEELING TO HELP A LADEE EEN DEESTRESS? NO?

NO, INDEED! I MEAN *YES!* YES, OF COURSE, I'M *WEELING*--- *I MEAN WILLING!*

AH! SO STRONG!

MADAM *BEAVAIR!*---HERE EES POGOS---HE EES HAPPY TO HELP A LADY--- SO I AM GET HEEM TO HELP *YOU* LIKE I EES PROMISE.

189 PAIRS OF PANTS? COULDN'T *SOME* OF YOUR CHILDREN RUN AROUND LIKE THE *RAW-NATURED-TADS* THEY IS?

HANG AWAY, SON! TALK DON'T WASH.

A DAY PASSES AND WHY NOT?

ONLY DAY I GITS A CHANCE TO VISIT MISS MAM'SELLE HEPZIBAH, I IS GOTTA *BABY-SIT YOU!* FOOEY!

BANG! I'LL GO *WITH YOU, UNCLE POGO---* BANG! BANG!

"IN DASH SIR *OSBRONK!* HE GRAB UP A PISTOL AN' FIRE AT THE FLEEIN' FORM OF REGIBALD ARGOOGLE! *BANG! BANG!"*

75

77

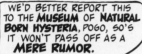

WHAT A **CRUEL** FATE FOR ONE SO **YOUNG**..

--- AN' **HAN'SOME.**

WHAT'S YOU BOATIN' UP **HERE** FOR, TURTLE?

JES' LOOK OUT FOR THAT **SEA SERPENT** DOWN THERE.

HEAR *THAT*? CALLED YOU A **SEA SERPENT.**

AFTER THAT, *I* DON'T EVEN B'LIEVE HE'S UP THAT TREE IN A **ROWBOAT!**

YOU SAY A **SEA SERPENT** CRAWLED OUT OF THE **WATER**? *WHAT'D* IT **LOOK** LIKE?

WELL--- FIERCE--- LIKE A **BULL** OR A **BUFFALO**--- OR A **RHINOCERWURST**--- BUT **MOSTLY** IT LOOKED LIKE A **SEA SERPENT.**

79

83

THIS IS NO MERE TINY BUG --- *MILWAUKEE IS A MENTAL GIANT* --- SUBTRACT **TWO FROM TWO,** MILWAUKEE --- (*WHAT'S HE SAY, ALBERT?*)

NOTHIN'

ZOUNDS! WHAT A BRAIN! THE RIGHT ANSWER IN THE **TWINK** OF AN EYE! AN INTELLECTUAL GOLIATH!

I'VE HAD AS MUCH TALK ABOUT YOUR BUG AS I CAN STAND --- *I AM HEADING WEST AGAIN!*

YOU, A **COW,** GOING **WEST?** WHY, THAT'S **COW** COUNTRY OUT **THERE!**

NATURALLY! I'M ALL SET --- *I AM A COW!* A FULL BLOODED, FOUR LEGGED, SQUARE RIGGED COW!

OKAY --- HAVE IT YOUR WAY --- LET'S HEAR YOU BELLER LIKE A COW.

GLADLY --- MEOW!

MEOW? *M-E-O-W? THAT'S* A COW NOISE?

WELL, IT GOES *SOMETHING LIKE THAT* --- I HAVEN'T REALLY HAD MUCH TIME TO PRACTICE.

I DON'T KNOW AS YOU'LL GO VERY FAR AS A **COW** IF YOU CAN'T MOO ANYTHING BUT *MEOW!*

I'LL TRY AGAIN.

MEE-ROWR!

HMM--- WELL, IT'S UNUSUAL, BUT NOT VERY *COWWY!*

HOW ARE YOU AT **CATCHING MICE?**

I NEVER TRIED--- BUT I'M YOUNG AND WILLING.

GOOD! THEN GO TO THIS ADDRESS IN **FORT MUDGE** AND SAY I SENT YOU---A LADY THERE IS LOOKING FOR A **CAT.**

GOSH---*BACK TO FORT MUDGE*---JUST BECAUSE I CAN'T MOO LIKE A **COW!** GONE IS THE IDLE DREAM OF THE *GOLDEN WEST!*

HOW DOES THAT COW CALL GO AGAIN, POGO?

MOO!

I'LL TRY ONCE MORE-- MEOW!

SORRY... YOU'D BETTER FACE IT AND TAKE THAT JOB IN FORT MUDGE CHASING MICE.

MY! MY! ARE MICE FIERCE?

NOT *EXACTLY*--- THEY'RE MORE *MOODY-LIKE!* YOU'LL NEVER HAVE A DULL MOMENT.

AH, THERE GOES A GOOD KID--- COULDN'T MAKE OUT AS A COW. WAS HEADIN' WEST FOR THE **BIG TIME** TOO.

DIDN'T HAVE THE VOICE, EH? KEPT MOOING, *"MEOW."*

YEP---AN' NOW IT'S BACK TO A HEART-BROKEN JOB AS A CAT.

MOOS IN TWO SYLLABLES, EH?

WELL, CHASING MICE WILL BE FUN.

HOW 'BOUT CAT FOOD? COWS DON'T EAT **MICE**---DOES SHE DRINK MILK?

GEE--- I NEVER THOUGHT TO ASK.

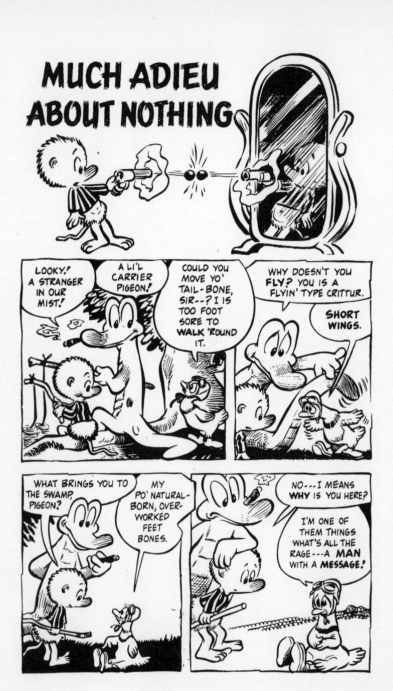

MUCH ADIEU ABOUT NOTHING

WHAT IS IT?

THAT'S WHAT THEY **DIN'T** DONE TOLE ME.

IT'S SUCH A **POW'FUL** SECRET NOBODY DIN'T EVEN DONE TELL ME **WHO'S** IT FOR.

BEEN KEEPIN' IT IN MY SHOE AN' IT'S KIND OF WORED OUT---*ONLY PART LEFT IS THE NAME.*

ANYBODY EVER HEAR OF A GENERAL WHAT GO BY NAME OF **LEE**--- *ROBERT E. LEE,* THAT IS?

H'LO, POGO.

HEY! OL' ALBERT AN' ME FOUND A **MAN WITH A MESSAGE**---A OL' CARRIER PIGEON WITH SHORT WINGS---HE'S A WALKIN' TYPE BIRD AN' HE WORED RIGHT ON THRU THE NOTE PAPER, 'COUNT OF HE TOTED IT IN HIS SHOE.

HERE'S ONE MUST BE IN ANOTHER LANGUAGE.

WHY, ALBERT, *THAT'S* **ENGLISH!**

ENGLISH? I ISN'T GONE BUY **ANY** MAIL WHAT'S WRIT IN A **FOREIGN** TONGUE---ISN'T YOU GOT **NONE** WHAT'S IN PLAIN **UNINETY STATES?**

YOU IS TRYIN' TO SELL MAIL AN' THIS ONE IS IN A FOREIGN LANGUAGE---I WANTS **MY MONEY BACK!**

YOU **DIN'T** PAY **NONE** YET.

A MERE **TECHNICALORIE!** LOOKY AT **THIS!**---THE *LANGUAGE OF A FOREIGN POWER!*

THAT'S **ENGLISH,** ALBERT---OUR NATIVE TONGUE!

AHA! YOU IS TRYIN' TO CONFUSE A HONEST CITIZEN! **ENGLISHMENS** IS FOREIGNERS, ISN'T THEY? **IS YOU A SPY?**

YES--- **I MEAN NO!** ISN'T ENGLISH OUR OWN LANGUAGE, PARTNER?

I DUNNO 'BOUT **THAT**---BUT YOU CAN KEEP YO' HAN'S TO YO' SELF--- **YOU IS ALWAYS** HAD A **SNEAKY LOOK!**

MAILMAN, IS YOU GOT A STIFF LETTER TO A CONGRESSMAN FOR SALE?

HAH!

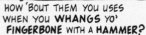

HOW 'BOUT THEM YOU USES WHEN YOU **WHANGS** YO' **FINGERBONE** WITH A **HAMMER**?

OH--- THEM?

LIES! EVASION! SUBTER- FUSE!

AT LAST HE GONE SWEAR HE **ISN'T** MEANT NO **DISRESPECT** TO OUR SOVEREIGNTY.

I SWEARS: GOSH-A-MICKLE DICKLE PICKLE DAG NAG AN'...

LOUDER!

AN' TAKE OFF YO' HAT!

DAG NAB YOU BLACKSTABBIN' BAGSTAGGERED OL' GOATS ANYHOWS!

ISN'T WE BEEN MORE SWORED **AT** THAN **WITH**?

I NOT SURE IS OUR NATIONAL HONOR BEEN VINDICATED OR LINQUIDATED.

THAT OUGHT TO TAKE CARE OF **YOU AN'** THE SWEARIN'!

MISS MAM'ZELLE HEPZIBAH, I IS BRUNG OVER MY FIANNCY.

AH! TRÉS BON! YOU SHOULD HAVE ZE SOCIETY WEDDING WEETH ZE GOWN AN' ZE FLOWAIR, NON?

YAS, INDEED! I GOT A TRAIN FOR THE WEDDIN.'

YOU GOTTA TRAIN? WHAT THIS GONE BE? A **CHAMPEENSHIP** FIGHT?

STOP SITTIN' THERE **SOAKIN'** YOUR FEET IN THE **TEA** AND HELP ME GET READY FOR OUR WEDDIN'.

BUT **THIS** IS THE BEST THING I'VE TRIED YET FOR MY **TIRED FOOTS!**

COME, MEESTAIR PEA-JEAN, OBSERVE! EEN THE SOUTH ZE GENTLEMEN REESENT WHEN A MAN DOES NOT GO THRU WEETH A MARRIAGE!

THEY AIN'T GONE RESENT IT HALF SO MUCH IF I DON'T DO IT AS I DOES DO IF I DO DOES!

HA, BUT YOU MAY FIND YOURSELF IN ZE DUEL!

IF I **DO**, IT WON'T BE **ME.**

FOOF! YOU HAVE NO **FLAIR!** YOU'RE NOT ZE DASHING TYPE!

GIMME A OPEN ROAD AND YOU GONE SEE SOME DASHIN' WHAT GOT A **REAL** FLAIR ON IT.

ALBAIRT, WHAT YOU THEENK OF A MAN WHAT DO NOT MARRY ZE GIRL WHEN HE EES PROMEES?

I THEENK HE EES ZE NO GOOD SKUNK...*OOP!* UH--I-MEAN--*SCALAWAG!*

HONAIR EES AT STAKE! HE SHOULD BE PUNEESH WEETH ZE SWORD!

WHO DID THIS TO **YOU?** I'LL DUEL HIM **FREE** OF **CHARGE!**

AH, SO STRONG! MY HERO! BUT EES NOT **ME** --- WHO EES DEESGRACE EES **MEEZ BEEVAIR!**

MEEZ BEEVAIR!?

SORRY, I IS GOT A PREVIOUS APPOINTMENT TO GO INTO THE ALLIGATOR BAG BUSINESS WITH A NICE OL' COUPLE IN HO-HO-KUS.

THERE'S A RUMOR GOIN' 'ROUND THAT US MEN IN THE SWAMP IS TOO **CRAVEN** TO FIGHT A DUEL.

THAT'S NOT **EXACTLY** A RUMOR.

MIZ MAMZELLE HEPZIBAH CLAIM THEY ISN'T **ONE** OF US SO **PURE OF SOUL** AND SO **COURAGEOUS OF HEART** TO UPHOLD THE **HONOR** OF THE **SWAMP!**

MAN! SHE SURE FIGGERED **US** TO THE BONE!

98

99

100

EVAIRSING EES ALL HOKAY! I HAVE FIND ZE CHOMPEEN WHO EES TO DEFEND ZE **HONAIR** OF ZE **COWARDLY** PEA-JEAN WHO EES **RUN AWAY!**

AN' THE **HONOR** OF THE **SWAMP** WHAT WAS **INSULTED** BY THE **CRAVEN BUM** IN THE **FIRST PLACE** WILL BE DEFENDED BY OUR **OTHER** CHAMPEEN--?

RIGHT.

AN' **POGO** IS THE CHAMPEEN WHO GONE DEFEND **OUR** HONOR AN' **MIZ BEAVER'S** HONOR WHO WAS INSULTED BY THE PIGEON BY NOT MARRYIN' HER.

RIGHT.

WHO'S THE CHAMPEEN WHAT GONE DEFEND THE **PIGEON'S** HONOR?

WHO ELSE?! **MEEZ BEEVAIR!**

YOU MEANS **POGO,** WHO **DON'T WANT** TO FIGHT A DUEL IN THE **FIRST PLACE, GOTTA** DEFEND THE **HONOR** OF **MIZ BEAVER** WHO WAS---

--- INSULTED BY THE **PIGEON** WHO RAN AWAY TO **WASHINGTON** TO BE A **BALL-HEADED IGGLE** AN' THAT LEAVES **NOBODY** FOR POGO TO **DUEL,** SO **SOMEBODY---**

- ---GOT TO STAND AN' UPHOLD THE **MIZZABLE PIGEON'S** HONOR AN' FIGHT POGO, AN' THE *ONLY ONE* **WILLIN'** TO DO IT IS---
- *NATURELLEMENT,* **MEEZ BEEVAIR!**
- IT DON'T MAKE SENSE!
- SENSE! *PHAUGH!* WE SPEAK OF HONAIR, M'SIEUR, **NOT SENSE!**

- WELL, **POGO,** IS YOU ALL READY FOR THE **DUEL?**
- YEP, I IS PRACTICED *FIRIN'* THE GUN, BUT DIDN'T GET TO **HIT** NOTHIN' YET 'CAUSE LOUD NOISES SCARES ME AN' I IS BEEN **FEARED** TO PULL THE TRIGGER.

- AT AIMIN' IT THOUGH, I IS A NATURAL BORNED **EXPERT!**
- YO' **LUNCH** WHAT IS ALL PACKED FO' THE **BIG DAY** IS MIGHTY **INNERESTIN'.**
- SINCE YOU IS FIGHTIN' THE DUEL AT DAWN, *YOU MIGHT NOT NEED NO LUNCH COME NOON---* SO I'LL KEEP IT 'TIL WE FINDS OUT AN' SAVE **YOU** THE WORRY OF IT.
- TURTLE, HOW CAN I *EVER* THANK YOU?

102

AH! IT WORKS JES' *GREAT!*

AN' WHO'S IN IT, ALBERT?

PLING!

THE **PARTY** WHAT OWNS IT IS THE **PARTY** WHAT'S IN IT AN' THE **PARTY** WHAT'S IN IT IS THE **PARTY** WHAT GONE WEAR IT TO THE DUEL AN' *THAT* PARTY IS THE **PARTY** WHAT GONE **PERFORM** OPPOSITE YOU **IN** THE DUEL.

US KIN WEAR WHAT US PLEASES.

THE **BIG DUEL DAY** IS HERE---AN' EVER'BODY IS HERE TO WISH POGO **GOOD B**Y---UH--I MEAN GOOD **LUCK!**

HERE Y'ARE---BALLOONS, FAVORS, SAN'WICHES--- SCORECARDS---Y'CAN'T TELL THE PLAYERS WITHOUT A SCORECARD SON.

I CAN-- I'M *IN* IT.

Now then, take your guns, folks.

KAPOW! *KAPOW!* *KAPOW!* *KAPUT!*

104

EVERY DAY
HAS ITS
DOG

THERE'S THE PUP-DOG ON HIS WAY TO *ALBERT'S HOUSE.* ALBERT IS MAD 'CAUSE THE PUP STOLE A STEAK.

THAT '*GATOR* DON'T LIKE BEIN' DISTURBED *WHEN HE ASLEEP.*

I SENT PUP DOG OVER TO ALBERT'S TO BORRY A CUP OF SUGAR A LONG TIME AGO --- HE OUGHT TO BE HOME.

HEY, ALBERT! WAKE UP! WHERE'S THE PUP DOG?

WHY, SON, *HE* NOT HERE

HE GONE?

I GUESS... ---- GONE ---

BLAG STAB IT! *DON'T FEEL* SO *BAD!* ISN'T WE SEARCHED THE SWAMP *ALL NIGHT* FOR THE LOST PUP DOG? US BETTER GIT HOME --- AN' TOMORRY'S ANOTHER DAY.

COME *ON!* YOU CAN'T SIT IN THE COLD --- AN' *I* ISN'T GONE *CARRY* YOU!

DAG BAG! POGO, I IS GONE 'LONG *WITHOUT* YOU.

OH--- *HOONK!*

SHHHHHHH

111

WELL, HAWGSHAW, THE TRAIL OF THE LOST PUP ENDS AT ALBERT'S HOUSE --- OUR HOUNDS WILL SEE IF IT GO 'LONG ANY FURTHER.

TOO BAD, ALBERT---- YES, THAT'S TOUGH LUCK.

WE MIGHTY UPSET 'BOUT THAT PUP-DOG, OWL.

OH..DON'T WORRY SO,--- MY DEAR SIR, ----THERE'S VERY LITTLE TO SHOW HE DISAPPEARED INTO YOUR HOUSE!

SO FAR YOU'RE IN THE CLEAR---OH, THERE'S THEM AS WHISPERS THE LI'L' PUP IS BEEN ATE! BUT, NO PROOF YET ---SO, CHIN UP OLD BOY --CHIN UP!

FROM WHAT I HEAR, THE LOST PUP DOG VANISHED AT ALBERT'S HOUSE---'COURSE ALBERT DIN'T LIKE THE TAD TOO WELL AN' ALBERT IS A ALLIGATOR BY TRADE.

OH, DON'T GIVE IT A-FIRST THOUGHT.

WELL, ALBERT IS MIGHTY WORRIED!

OOG

NOTCHERWELLY, THE BLOODHOUND IS TOO *BOSSY*---HE GOES WHERE *HE* WANTS--- FOLLOWS HIS *OWN* NOSE WITH NO, BUT *UTTERWELLY, NO* EYE-MAGINATIONS.

WITH WELL-MANNERED DOGS, *NOTCHERWELLY,* SUCH IS NOT A PROBLEM.

The point is well taken!

THEY CAN'T TAKE IT TOO FAR FOR ME.

AND, WHILE THE SEARCH GOES ON..

A *PUPPY!* WHAT ARE YOU IN FOR? YOU LOOK KINDA SAD, KIDDO.

WURF!

..We find the pup detained in sad and secret Durance Vile.

WANNA GIT *SPRUNG,* SON? I'LL SHOW YOU MY PRIVATE EXIT. IS IT A LITTLE SNUG?---OOMPH ---I'M AFRAID, MY BOY, THAT, UNLESS WE BLAST, IT WON'T WORK.

DON'T FRET, OLD SOLDIER, IF YOU'RE *IN*...YOU'RE *IN*-- I'LL GET SOME GRUB AN' WE'LL SPEND THE NIGHT SINGING AND TELLING LIES.

I MIND ONE TIME I STOP OVER IN FRISCO AND THERE'S THE STUPIDEST LOOKIN' CAT SITTIN' IN A BAKE SHOP WINDOW ---*WELL, SIR,* I ----- *BLOW ME DOWN!* HE'S ASLEEP! WELL, HE'S YOUNG AND NOT MUCH FOR *INTELLECTUAL DISCUSSION.*

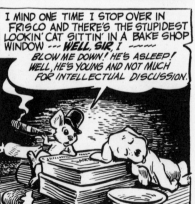

Looking for the lost dog, *eh? Well! Every-*
one thinks **Albert Ate** *the poor lad* ~
The Investigators *express grave*
fears ~~~~ O! *I shall* **demand**
custody of the **Child!** *No cannibal*
is a fit guardian.

HOW CAN **YOU**
BE IN CHARGE
OF A PUP WHAT
IS **ALREADY**
ET BY ALBERT?

~ *Well! There's* **duplicity**
for you! **See** *how*
cunning and under-
handed he is? ~~

You'll be glad to know there's no need searching for the lost pup any more ~ The Investigators have decided that Albert ate him ~ Owl will serve as Judge; Turtle and Myself will be on the Jury so we can Convict Albert with a Fair Trial

GOOD! THINGS OUGHT TO BE FAIR.

IT'S INTERESTING TO KNOW THAT THE CONFIDENCE OF IGNORANCE HAS NOT DIED OUT!

BIG WORDS OF PRAISE MAKE ME GIGGLE AN' SNEEZE.

You must learn to accept gracefully the plaudits of a grateful community

THERE GO THE INVESTIGATORS TRYIN' TO PIN THE PUP'S DISAPPEAR-ANCE ON ALBERT.

THEY SAYS THEY IS GOT PROOF THE PUP DOG VANISHED INTO HIS HOUSE.

IT HARD TO FIGGER

A LI'L' DOG DISAPPEARS NEAR A CRITTUR WHAT COMES FROM A FAMBLY WHAT **EATS ANYTHING.** ---AND **THAT** LI'L' DOG IS **NEVER SEED AGAIN.**

WHAT'S A BODY TO THINK?

I HEARD YO' LAST *REF-MARK,* PORKY---LET'S **FACE FACTS!** *STOP SHILLY-SHALLYIN' !* THE CRITTUR YOU MENTION **GOTTA** BE GUILTY---*HE JUS' MUST OF ET* THE PUP DOG --- AN' I DON'T *CARE* **WHO** HE IS !

IT'S ABOUT TIME **JUSTICE** WAS DID---IF SOMEBUDDY *ATE* THAT PUP DOG, **SOMEBODY** GOTTA **PAY!** THE GUILTY SHOULD BE PUNISHED! ---DAG **BLAG IT!** STOP DRAGGIN' YO' TAIL, POGO~

OOOMPH!

LET THE BLAME FALL WHERE SHE MAY, ALBERT?

Y BONDS

THE LIBERTY BELLE

WHERE-*EVER* SHE MAY! I IS FIRM! WHO DOES THE UNVESTIGATORS SUSPECK? *WHERE* DO THE FINGER-BONE POINT? *WHO'S THE ONE?* IT MATTER NOT--- BUT **WHO?**

WELL, HE'S IN THIS BOAT.

THE LIBERTY BELLE

Y'KNOW, A SUSPECKED MAN FINALLY GIT FEELIN' LIKE HE MUST OF DID *SOME* THIN'--- I GONE OFF~ Y'ALL DON'T WANT *ME* AROUND--

HEY, ALBERT!

AW---

ALBERT, OL' UNVESTIGATORS BACK THERE GONE ARREST YOU AN' BEAT A **CONFESSION** OUTEN YOU --- I SNUCK ON OFF TO TELL YOU 'CASE YOU WANTS CUT AN' RUN.

THANK YOU, TURTLE.

COME ON THIS WAY ALBERT! POGO AN' ME KIN *HIDE* YOU IN TH' MOST DEEP SWAMP AN'---

NOPE- WHERE'S YO' MANNERS, CHILLUN? IF A COUPLE STRANGERS WISHES TO INTERR**O**GATE A SOUTHERN GENTLE-MAN, *THEY GITS THEIR CHANCE*... I GONE STROLL OVER THIS WAY.

WE'S GONE YOUR WAY, TOO.

Meanwhile, in the mysterious dungeon ~~

HELLO, PARD! I BRUNG SOME PAPER HATS AN' FAVORS ----- TIME YOU WAS CHEERED UP WITH A LITTLE PARTY.

HAVE A COOKIE, KID --- YOU LOOK GREAT IN THAT OUTFIT ---- *CHEER UP!* OPEN YOUR FAVORS.

THIS SHOULD HAND YOU A LAUGH, PAL; ON THE OUTSIDE A COUPLA SNOOPS ARE HORSIN' AROUND LOOKIN' FOR A LOST KID --- *BIG REWARD* AN' ALL --- NEITHER ONE COULD FIND HIS OWN HEAD WITH BOTH HANDS AND A ROAD MAP --- *HAW HAW!*

WOULDN'T MIND FINDIN' HIM MYSELF --- *YOU AN' ME WOULD BE EATIN' HIGH ON THE HOG, KID.*

HEY! WHAT'S THE BLEACHERS FOR? A BALL GAME? WHERE'S THEM OL' UNVESTIGATORS?

'TAINT BLEACHERS; IT'S A JURY BOX -- UNVESTIGATORS GONE THROW A BIG OL' TRIAL.

A TRIAL?

OF WHO?

OF YOU.

HEY --- FETCH SOME BRANCH WATER!

WHAT'S A MATTER *HIM?*

DON'T TAKE LIFE SO SERIOUS, SON --- IT AIN'T *NO HOW* PERMANENT.

123

AS ALBERT'S LAWYER, I GOTTA QUESTION ALL THE JURY MEMBERS, MIZ LIMPKIN; I HOPES YOU HASN'T DECIDED THAT ALBERT'S GONE BE FOUND *GUILTY* LIKE MOST FOLKS HAS.

I MOST CERTAINLY HAS *NOT* DECIDED HE'S GONE BE FOUND *GUILTY.*

GOOD FOR YOU, MIZ LIMPKIN.

'COURSE I MUS' SAY, ON THE OTHER HAND, I CERTAINLY *HAS* MADE UP MY MIND THAT HE COULD *NEVER* BE FOUND "NOT GUILTY".

ALL RIGHT, LET'S GIT GOIN' WITH TH' TRIAL! COURT'S OPEN FOR BUSINESS.

IS THE JURY READY WITH THE GUILTY VERDICK YET? LET'S NOT DILLY DALLY.

JUST FOR LAUGHS, OWL, LET'S ASK A FEW QUESTIONS FIRST.

THE LIBERTY BELLE

BUY BONDS

475 HIT THIS SIGN WITH A BATTED BALL AND WIN A NEW SUIT.

SMOKE OLD GROGS

126

In the secret dungeon ~

JUDGE OWL, I GOT A WITNESS WHAT JUS' LEARNED IN SCHOOL 'BOUT *LIBERTY,* *FAIR TRIAL* AN OTHER *TRIVIA.*

THE LIBERTY BELLE

BUY THEM OL' BONDS

WELL, UM --- IT'S FROM A OL' **DECLARATION** --- IT GOES -UM- *"We hold these truths -* um - *to be self-* MM- *EVIDENT* ---uh- **ALL** *men are --* uh- *created equal --- um--- with certain in-* um- *in-alienable rights !...*

I OBJECT! I OBJECT! THIS IS UN-CONSTITUTABLE AN --

"THAT AMONG THESE ARE --- UH- WELL-NOW MM - UH - UM ---

BUY THEM OL' BOND

psst--- *"LIFE LIBERTY AN' THE PURSUIT OF HAPPINESS..."*

SURE 'NUFF, JUDGE, BUT SPEAK RIGHT OUT ---'T'AINT NOTHIN' TO BE 'SHAMED OF.

NOW JUST SUPPOSE WE HAD FOUND A MESSAGE WRITTEN IN SPANISH (BY *ALBERT*) CONFESSING THAT **HE** WAS THE CULPRIT!

I OBJECT!

MY CLIENT CAN'T WRITE IN *SPANISH!*

ITALIAN?

NO!

FRENCH?

NO!

SAMSKRIP?

NO!

128

TEN FOOT POLL TAX

"LOOKY! LOOKY! A POO-RADE!"

VOTE FOR OWL

A VOTE FOR O.W.L.

"YOU OUT TO GIT *EELECTED* TO SOMETHIN' OWL? WHAT'S YOU FOR?"

"I IS FOR *ME* MOSTLY, BUT ALSO FOR *WIMMIN AND CHILLUN SUFFRAGE.*"

"YOU DON'T GIT *MY* VOTE --- WIMMIN AN' CHILLUN *SUFFERS* PLENTY AS IT GO NOW."

"IF JOKES COULD *VOTE,* *THAT* ONE WOULD OF CAST A BALLOT FOR *TIPPECANOE TYLER!*"

IS A VOTE FOR Y-O-U

"Ahem! Some of the voters are urging Me to run."

"WHICH WAY? WHAT YOU BEEN UP TO, DEACON?"

VOTE FOR OWL

"Elections are coming up.... These are perilous times --We need strong hands-- and I have always had a flair for Foreign Relations"

NOW, BEFORE I CLOSE MY **BRILLIANT CAMPAIGN** SPEECH TO THE FRENZIED CHEERS OF YOU **ADMIRERS**--- *IS THEY ANY QUESTIONS?*

YES, **WHAT** IS YOU RUNNIN' FOR?

HMM--- **WELL!** A **VERY** GOOD QUESTION---WELL, I'M RUNNIN' FOR **PUBLIC OFFICE** ON ACCOUNT I IS GONE BE **SOMEBODY IMPORTANT!**---INSTEAD OF A COMMON ORNERY TYPE OF LOW LIFE LIKE---

LIKE **WHO?**

WELL---UM---

LIKE ORNERY CITIZENS?

SO TO SPEAK--- **SO** TO SPEAK.

THE LOW TYPE GITS UP TO BAT **SOON** OWL, THEN YOU'LL FIND OUT WHO'S **REALLY** IMPORTANT.

GOSH--- POGO TALKIN' 'BOUT **US.'**

NATURAL

COME WASH YO' FACE AN' PUT ON A CLEAN COLLAR--- WE GOIN' TO **VOTE.**

VOTE!? I ISN'T GONE DISCOMFORT **MY SELF** JES' TO VOTE FOR A PARCEL OF **MUTTON HEADS!**

WELL, I IS ALL DRESSED UP AND IS PACKED A NICE LUNCH--- AN' BESIDES IT'S YOUR **DUTY!**

HAH! I OWE **NOTHING** TO THESE POLITICAL **POLTROONS!** I WOULDN'T VOTE FOR 'EM FOR **DOG CATCHER!**

A STIRRING TALE

OL' MAW GIT MESSIN' WITH A CAKE AN' PERTY SOON SHE GOT A *TUB* FULL OF PANS AN' SPOONS ALL STICKIED AN' *GOO*ED UP. *WHO GONE LICK 'EM CLEAN*, SON?

OH--- 'COURSE! SHE *DOUBLE DO* NEED *TADS* FOR *THAT* KIND WORK.

OH, *SURE!* THEY IS NO *TWO* WAYS 'BOUT IT!

BEHOLE, MIZ MUSHRAT! *WE IS IN THE CAKE STIRRIN' BUSINESS.*

WHILE ALBERT LOWERS *MORT* INTO THE BATTER, I RECITES *STIRRIN' POETRY* ---

"*Oh, whence that wince, My Wench?*" quoth I; She blushed an' said: "*Oh, Sir* ~~~

"*My old Daddy isn't stirrin' since my momma's been in Stir* ~~"
GLOP!

WOK

PULL ME OUT PULL ME OUT PULL ME OUT

Whooie -- THAT CAKE WAS *SO* SPICERY I MIGHTY NIGH BURNED OFF MY FEET OFF!

POWERFUL TASTY THO', MORT LESS *IT'S JES' YOU!*

HEY, POGO, WE'LL STIR YOUR CAKE FOR YOU!

MOULDY MORT IS TAKIN' HIS LI'L BOY NEPHEW, LOUIE THE TAD POLE, ALONG TO LEARN THE CAKE STIRRIN' PERFESSION.

HOLD IT! HOLD IT! YOU GOTTA DUMP THE WORKS OUT--- I IS LOST TOUCH WITH LI'L LOUIE AN' CAN'T FEEL THE DIFFERNTS 'TWEEN HIM AN' THE RAISINS.

RAISINS IS MORE WRINKLY.

MY BEST DAMASK TABLE CLOTH!

DON'T TAKE ON SO, POGO--WE'LL LICK IT ALL OFF!

LOUIE! LOUIE! IS THAT YOU?

GOTTA GIT MIZ HOPFROG! MOULDY MORT TOOK HER TAD INTO THE CAKE BATTER AN' GOT HIM MIXED UP WITH THE RAISINS!

YOUR OTHER LI'L CHILE IS TANGLED INTO THE CAKE BATTER, MIZ HOPFROG--DOES YOU KNOW YO' OWN TADS?

YEP! AIN'T GOT BUT ONE THO'--- THIS IS HIM--- A MAMMY'S LOVIN' HEART KNOWS HER OWN CHILE.

H'LO, SISTER, **YOU IS** GOT **MY** LI'L GIRL TAD THERE ---MOULDY MORT TOOK **YOUR** CHILE OFF THIS MORNIN'.

HE MIXED IN WITH RAISINS.

QUICK, **POGO!** WHICH WAY TO THE CAKE BATTER? A MAMMY'S LOVIN' HEART KIN SEPARATE HER CHILE FROM THE RAISINS IN A TWINKLE.

ARF AN' ARF

IN A TWINKLE OF A EYE I CAN PICK OUT MY OWN LI'L BOY, **LOUIE**, FROM OUT THIS MESS OF BATTER AN' RAISINS!

BEHOLE! I PLUCKS HIM FROM THE RUBBLE BY THE TAILBONE!

THEY'S NOTHIN' LIKE A MAMMY'S LOVIN' HEART.

SEE HOW **SMART** HE IS? GOOD OL' LOUIE!

JES' A DAGBAGGED MINUTE!

HERE'S OL' LOUIE---YO' MAMMY'S LOVIN' HEART IS PICKED OUT A RAISIN!

NEXT TIME TAKE THE STEMS OFFA YO' RAISINS.

YOU COULD *STILL* FOOL ME!

BEWITCHED, BOTHERED AND BEMILDRED

WELL, MR. BAT, IF YOU WANTS TO RENT THAT *VACANCY* YOU **CAN---**

HOW 'BOUT THIS *DRAFT?*

IT STOPS WHEN YOU CLOSES THE DOOR.

I'LL TRY IT.

HOW'S THAT?

GREAT!

AH, **WHOOMP!?**

HEY! I ISN'T GONE TAKE THIS PLACE IF IT GOT NOISY NEIGHBORS!

I **RENTED** THIS SPACE INSIDE YO' **MOUTH** FROM YO' NEPHEW, ALBERT, AN', BY JING, I IS GONNA **STAY!**

I WAS HERE **FIRST!**

SQUATTERS RIGHTS GOT *NOTHIN'* TO DO WITH IT!

UNCLE ALBERT IS TRYIN' TO EVICT A BAT.

WELL, I ISN'T GONNA HAVE NO BATS LIVIN' **INSIDE MY HEAD!**

WHERE'S YO' **SOUTHERN HOSPARTILLERY**, ALBERT?

HOW WOULD **YOU** LIKE TO HAVE **BATS**?

FO' **SHAME!**

HOW **CRUEL!** CHUNKIN' OUT A POOR, HOMELESS BAT!

YEAH! AN' A **WIDOWER** AT **THAT**.

ALL RIGHT! BUT, BY NED, YOU GOTTA TAKE OFF YO' HAT!

WHY DOESN'T YOU MIGRATE LIKE **OTHER** BIRDS?

BATS ISN'T STRICTLY **BIRDS**.

COULDN'T YOU TAKE A **TRIP** ANYWAYS? WHY NOT GO SEE YOUR **COUSINS** IN **CARLSBAD CAVERNS**?

WELL--- US **BATS** **DO** VISIT EACH OTHER.

THEN **GO! GO!** I CAN SPARE YOU--- I CAN **SACRIFICE MYSELF** TO A LIFE OF **LONELINESS!**

IT AIN'T GONNA BE NECESS-ARY.

HERE COMES SOME OF THE BOYS NOW----**ALL THE WAY FROM CARLSBAD JUST TO VISIT ME!** OH, WHAT A LUCKY DAY FOR YOU, ALBERT!

SO, MALLARD DE MER, YOU GETS *SEASICK* WHEN YOU SWIMS?

YEP... AN' WET.

I'LL GO HOME AN' STOP *CROWDIN'* UP THE *PANELS*... G'BYE ALL.

I *HATES* BEIN' WET LIKE A CAT.

SO YOU IS MIGRATIN' NORTH BY *KIDDIE CAR?*

YEP --- BUT *THIS* IS AS *FAR* AS I GO... THE *END* OF THE LINE --- I IS COMED *ALL THE WAY FROM MIAMI.*

WELL, THIS AIN'T EXACTLY *ESKIMO* COUNTRY.

IT'S NORTH ENOUGH FOR *ME* --- I DON'T WANNA GO RIPPIN' THRU THEM *NORTHERN* CITIES SCARIN' THE *GENTRY* AN' *LIVESTOCK.*

THEY *STARTLES* EASY UP THAT WAY.

ACTUAL, I IS COMED UP FOR A MEETING OF THE *AUDIBLE BOY BIRD WATCHERS SOCIETY.*

THAT SO, MR. *MALLARD DE MER?*

YEP, *DEACON MUSHRAT* IS A *CAPTAIN* OF THE *BIRD WATCHERS.* HE SAY WE GOT A *MESS OF WATCHIN'* TO DO UP HERE.

BUSINESS SORT OF *PILED* UP?

OH, **YES INDEED!** HE SAY BIRDS IS UP HERE WHAT **NEVER IS** BEEN **WATCHED!** WE IS **WAY** BEHIND ON OUR WORK.

HE OVER WATCHIN' **ALBERT** NOW.

ALBERT IS NOT **PREE-**ZACKLY A BIRD---HE MORE OF A ALLIGORATOR---BUT HE GOT A MOUTHFUL OF **BATS** AN' THEY IS **SOMEWHAT** BIRDS.

MAN! THINGS IS BAD!

CADET MALLARD DE MER OF THE AUDIBLE BOY BIRD WATCHERS SOCIETY REPORTING, SIR.

Good Work, Cadet De Mer ~~ You is *Jest* in time ~~ I been watchin' these bats 'til I is ready to drop.

ANOTHER SNOOP!

HAS YOU BEEN ABLE TO **IDENTIFY** 'EM YET, SIR?

AAHH, YOU LI'L PEEP, WE KIN **INDENTIFY** *OUR* SELFS! I'M **BEWITCHED!**

I'M **BOTHERED!**

I'M **BEWILDERED**

WE'RE **ALL BATS.**

HOW YOU SPELLS **BEMILDRED?**

A **UNDER-**STATEMINTS.

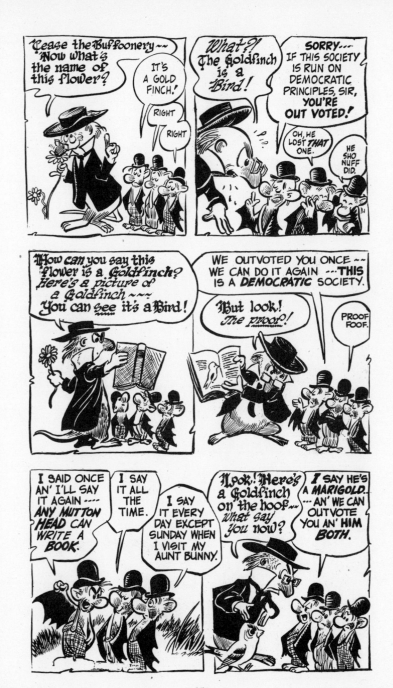

153

156

AN'---IF I'M NOT MISTAKEN, YOU ARE LIKELY TO BE HERE FOR SOME TIME?

I'm so trussed I can't move my Adam's apple.

GOOD! IF YOU'RE SUCH A GOOD BIRD WATCHER YOU CAN WATCH MY CHILDREN WHILE I GO TO THE LADIES AID MEETING.

eggs?

MALLARD DE MER, THE SEA SICK DUCK!

RIGHT! I RUSHED OVER TO TELL YOU THAT THE BOY BIRD WATCHERS IS LOST IN THE SWAMP!

THIS IS A JOB FOR MAN'S BEST FRIEND, NAMELY, THE DOG! ONLY HIS KEEN NOSE, HIS SPLENDID JUDGEMENT WILL FIND THE POOR, LOST CREE-TYOORS!

Here I am, bound helplessly by my Boy Bird Watchers in a knot-tying test ~~~ Left to watch two EGGS! Phoo! Back to the Tenderfoot Test ~~~ Watching eggs!

I'll just nap off for forty winks and recover my poise.

CRICK!

CRACK!

158

159

IN CASE YOU IS *WORRIED*, US GOT OL' DEACON MUSHRAT UNTIED FROM THE KNOTS YOU *BOY BIRD WATCHERS* TIED ...... BUT **NOW** WE IS LOOKIN' FOR MIZ LIMPKIN'S CHILLUN... *EITHER TWO EGGS OR NEW-HATCHED BIRDS*...IS YOU SEED 'EM?

TWO *EGGS*? OR NEW HATCHED BIRDS....MM? NOPE, ISN'T SEED **HIDE** NOR HAIR.

NOR NOTHIN'.

BAIT

IT'S ALL RIGHT FOR YOU YOUNG'UNS TO COME ON OUTEN THERE ---- THE POSSE IS GONE.

US DON'T GOTTA **GO**?

NOSSIRREE! 'TAINT FAIR FOR YOU TO LEAVE WHILE YOU IS FAR AHEAD! *WHOSE DEAL*?

NEMMINE WHOSE *DEAL*----WHOSE CARDS IS WHAT WORRIES ME.

THAT'S ALL **OKEFENOKEE** WITH US, SIRS... THIS IS A VERY **ABSORBIN'** GAME YOU IS TEACHIN' US.

BAIT AND LUNCH

BAIT AND LUNCH

HERE I GO SPEEDIN' THRU THE SWAMP TO GIT HOME AN' FOTCH BACK MIZ LIMPKIN'S EGGS ----*GANGWAY!*

WHERE IS **I** GOIN'? I DON'T LIVE IN THE SWAMP NOHOW! AN' *WHAT'S* **MORE** THEM EGGS WOULDN'T BE HOME IF I GOT THERE.

EGGS? NEED EGGS?

LITTLE POLTERGEISTS SHOULD BE SEEN AND NOT HEARD

Panel 1: HE'LL *NEVER* LEARN TO HUNT! LOOK, HE'S POINTIN' ANOTHER *GRASS* HOPPER!

TADS ISN'T LIKE THEY WAS IN *MY* TIME.

Panel 2: YEP! IT'S *PLAY!* *PLAY!* *PLAY!* NEVER LEARN A TRADE-- *OH, NO!*

HE'S NO HUNTER.

SHHH

Panel 3: I TRY TO BE FAIR--I SAY: THE YOUTH TODAY ISN'T AS *STUPID* AS IT LOOKS---GIVE 'EM A CHANCE, I SAY--- AND *THEN, BANG!*

THANKS, KID, HERE'S A LI'L TOKEN.

Panel 4: *THIS* HAPPENS--- *WE'RE LOOKIN'* FOR *BIRDS---* HE FINDS *CIGARS!*

TSK TSK TSK

DON'T RUSH THE PUP--- BRING HIM ALONG SLOW--- TEACH HIM TO FETCH--- --NOW, *FETCH!*

FETCH, BOY.

TODAY, HOUN' DOG, *MAKE BELIEVE* YOU *SHOOTS* A BIRD AN' SEE IF OL' PUP DOG GOIN' FETCH IT.

KAPOW
KAPOW
KAPOW!

SOME DAYS *NOTHIN'* WORKS OUT!

US SHOULDN'T EXPECT *TOO* MUCH FROM TADS, POGO. *SO,* I GOT HERE A PERFECTLY **SIMPLE** *INTELLIGENCE TEST* FOR A CHILE.

NOW THEN, PUP DOG, THE PROBLEM IS TO PUT THE RIGHT PIECE IN THE RIGHT HOLE---*I'LL* RUN THRU IT FIRST SO *YOU* GITS THE *IDEA*-- ---UM--WELL--WELL--HA, HA--SAY, THIS *IS A LI'L TRICKY--HA-HA--*

PSST, POGO-- *ANY DIRECTIONS OR SOLUTIONS PRINTED INSIDE THE COVER?* 'COURSE, I CAN HANDLE THIS OKAY---BUT A ANSWER WOULD SORTA *SPEED THINGS UP.*

NOPE--- NO SOLUTIONS PRINTED IN IT---

BY NAB! HOW THEM GAME COMPANIES *EXPECK* US *TUTORS* TO KNOW WHEN THE LI'L TADS GIT IT RIGHT?

BRAIN TEST *for* INFANTS

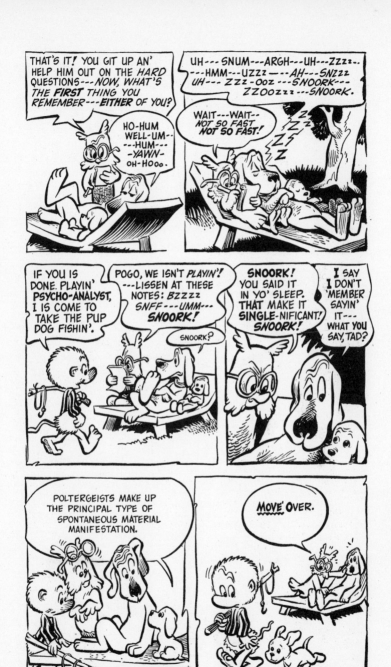

169

JUS' RELAX, EAT THE APPLE AN' TELL ME YOUR EARLY LIFE STORY---

FIRST THING I REMEMBER, MA LOOK IN THE DOOR AN' SAY: --OOP!

WHAT IN THE FOGGY BLUE MORNIN' IS A-GOIN' ON HERE?

MY LAND! SHE HAD QUITE A DEEP VOICE! WHAT ELSE SHE SAY?

BEEN SWIMMIN' UNDER WATER ALL DAY COUNTIN' POLLYWOGS FOR THE SCHOOL BOARD----- RUNNED OUT OF FINGERS! SHOULDA HAD EIGHT ARMS!

YO' MAMMY SAY THAT? A CLEAN CUT OCTOPUS COMPLEX! EIGHT ARMS!

SOMETHIN' I NEVER NOTICED BEFORE--- YOU IS GOT FEETS LIKE A ALLIGATOR.

DADDY AND MA HAD 'EM, TOO.

ZOUNDS! I MUST COMMUNICATE WITH VIENNA ON THIS!

I THOUGHT YOU WAS OL' BEAUREGARD, WHEN I WAS PSYCHO-ANALYZIN' YOU---

NO--- YOU CAN TELL THE DIFFERMINTS 'CAUSE MY NAME IS ALBERT!

SAY!

DO YOU KNOW THE PUP-DOG SPOKE? WE HAVE A TALKING DOG! WE CAN TOUR EUROPE'S ROYAL COURTS! WHY, THE BRAIN WHIRLS! WE MIGHT EVEN GET TO EXHIBIT AT SUPER-MARKET OPENINGS!

GADFLY! WHAT'D HE SAY?

"POLTERGEISTS MAKE UP THE PRINCIPAL TYPE OF SPONTANEOUS MATERIAL MANIFESTATION."

IT'S NOT EXACTLY A *ROUSER.* --- ANYTHING ELSE?

THAT'S ALL-- "POLTERGEISTS ETC.---"

SORRY; WHAT WOULD HE *EVER* DO FOR A *ENCORE?*

OH WELL, IT WAS A NICE DREAM.

AS LONG AS THE PUP-DOG CAN *TALK,* POGO, WE'RE GOING TO TAKE HIM ON A VAUDEVILLE TOUR.

NATURALLY, *I'LL* GO ALONG AS THE CHILD'S *GUARDIAN* --- I KNOW A FEW MAGIC TRICKS! WATCH *THIS* ONE --- I BREAK AN EGG INTO MY PLUG HAT---

I MIX IT THOROUGHLY--- *THEN,* WITHOUT HARMING THE HAT--- I ----UH---WELL, *WELL* ---HMM.---

YOUR TRICK *SMELLS* GOOD---IS IT *DONE* YET?

THE TEACHER SAY: "MY, AREN'T YOU *WARM*?" *(THAT'S ANOTHER TWO)* CHOMP---

RIGHT--- *SIX* UP TO NOW.

WELL? WHAT'S THE LAST LINE? THE *PAYOFF*? THE *BOFF*?

DING BING IT*!* *I NEVER CAN REMEMBER THE LAST LINES OF JOKES---* CHOMP--- CHOMP---

POLTERGEISTS MAKE UP THE PRINCIPAL TYPE OF MATERIAL MANIFESTATION.

MAN! THAT LINE IS DRIVIN' ME CRAZY!

LET'S TEACH HIM HIS ACT.

NOW, WHEN WE SPEAK TO *YOU* AFTER THE MUSIC DIES DOWN, PUP, *YOU ANSWER:* "I JUST GOT BACK FROM THE ANIMAL SHOW!"

ALL RIGHT--- NOW YOU GOT IT*!*

♫♫ *HEAR THAT WHISTLE PUFF AND BLOW--* ♫♫ *AS WE RIDE ON OUT OF BUFF·A·LO?* ♫

*HEH*LO, JOE, WHAT D'YA KNOW?

POLTERGEISTS MAKE UP THE PRINCIPAL TYPE OF MATERIAL MANIFESTATION.

WHAT OUTSTANDING ACT CAN WE CLOSE OUR VAUDEVILLE PROGRAM WITH?---THE PUP DOG WILL SPEAK---AN' THEN---AN' THEN---

I'LL SING!

Oh, wistfully blissly, Blithely I bless The sanguinely songing Of my sister Bess--- For longingly lightly And lissomely low The sowing of soda is ever so --so -----

SO! THIS GIVES ME A GREAT IDEA FOR A FINISH! LIE DOWN, TURTLE!

LIKE SO?

LIKE SO.

HEY! NO FAIR! YOU CAN'T SAW A MUSICIAN IN HALF!

NOW, THE FIRST VAUDEVILLE TRICK THE PUP DOG WILL DO IS ADD A FEW SUMS--- NOW, HOW MUCH IS ONE AND ONE, LI'L DOG?

WURF! WURF!

GREAT! TWO BARKS! NOW, HOW MUCH IS---

WAIT! WAIT! NOT SO FAST! LET'S FIGGER OUT IF THE FIRST ANSWER IS RIGHT!

THE ATLANTA BELLE

174

A Merry Very Crispness

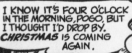

I KNOW IT'S FOUR O'CLOCK IN THE MORNING, POGO, BUT I THOUGHT I'D DROP BY. *CHRISTMAS* IS COMING AGAIN.

WHA'?

IT'S AN EVER PRESENT NUISANCE. I *DON'T LIKE ANYBODY* ---'CEPT ONE CRITTUR WHOM I DISLIKES *LESS* THAN MOST --- BEEN SAVING SOMETHIN' FOR HIM SINCE AUGUST.

A BLUNT INSTRUMENT?

A *DAISY!* IT'S YOURS --- DON'T THANK ME --- I HATE FAWNING, MAUDLIN SENTIMENT. YOU DON'T SEE DAISIES AT THIS TIME OF THE YEAR --- --- I ENJOYED THIS ONE, MAYBE YOU WILL, TOO.

KEEP IT AND HAVE A MERRY CHRISTMAS --- IF THE REST OF THE SWAMP CRITTURS DON'T LIKE YOU ANY BETTER THAN I DO, YOU WON'T GET A SIMPLE GOOD MORNING.

THANK YOU, ... YOU OL' PORKYPINE.